The Best **Recorder D**
Book Ever!
Selected and edited by **Emma Coulthard**

Chester Music

Contents

Twinkle twinkle little star

Traditional
arr. Emma Coulthard

Anglaise

English, 18th century
arr. Emma Coulthard

Scarborough Fair

English folk song
arr. Emma Coulthard

Theme from *The New World Symphony*

Antonín Dvořák
arr. Emma Coulthard

That Sounds So Beautiful
from *The Magic Flute*

Wolfgang Amadeus Mozart
arr. Wilhelm Popp

Stella Splendens
(Shining Star)

Spanish, 14th century
arr. Emma Coulthard

Zum Gali Gali

Israeli song
arr. Emma Coulthard

Minuet

James Hook, Op. 37 No. 2
arr. Emma Coulthard

Supercalifragilisticexpialidocious
from *Mary Poppins*

Richard M. Sherman &
Robert B. Sherman
arr. Emma Coulthard

Chim Chim Cher-ee
from *Mary Poppins*

Richard M. Sherman &
Robert B. Sherman
arr. Emma Coulthard

I Have a Dream

Benny Andersson & Björn Ulvaeus
arr. Emma Coulthard

Hornpipe
from *Water Music*

George Frideric Handel
arr. Emma Coulthard

Dona Nobis Pacem

Giovanni Palestrina

12

The Charms of Love

Cesare Negri
arr. Emma Coulthard

The Last Rose of Summer

Irish folk song
arr. Emma Coulthard

The Lonely Goatherd
from *The Sound of Music*

Richard Rodgers
arr. Emma Coulthard

Round Dance
from *For Children*

Béla Bartók
arr. Emma Coulthard

Menuetto

Carl Stamitz, Op. 27

Descant

Descant

Simple Gifts

Traditional
arr. Emma Coulthard

Somewhere Out There
from *An American Tale*

James Horner, Barry Mann
& Cynthia Weil
arr. Emma Coulthard

Swing Low Sweet Chariot
& Nobody Knows De Trouble I See

Spirituals
arr. Emma Coulthard

Autumn Song

John Buckley

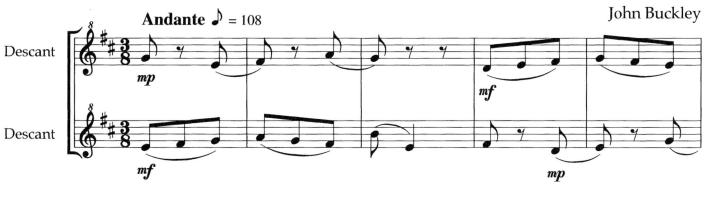

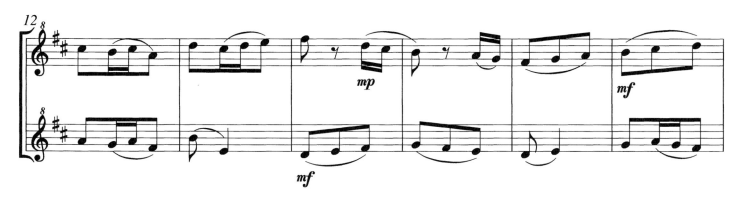

Virelai

Guillaume de Machaut
arr. Emma Coulthard

Evening Prayer
from *Hansel and Gretel*

Engelbert Humperdinck
arr. Michael McCartney

My Favourite Things
from *The Sound of Music*

Richard Rodgers
arr. Emma Coulthard

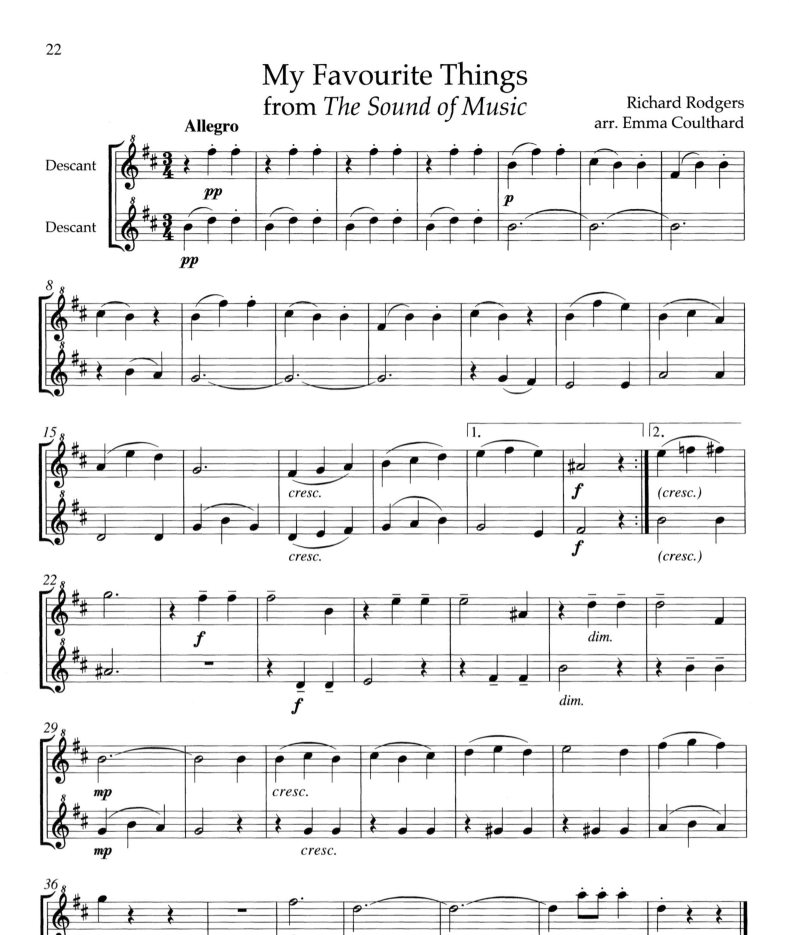

Two Little Pieces
1. A Sad Tale

Dmitri Kabalevsky
arr. Emma Coulthard

2. A Little Scherzo

Mamma Mia!

Benny Andersson,
Björn Ulvaeus & Stig Andersson
arr. Emma Coulthard

Lewis Bridal Song

Scottish folk song
arr. Emma Coulthard

Spring

John Buckley

Leave Now Mine Eyes Lamenting
Canzonetta

Thomas Morley
arr. Emma Coulthard

Sweet Nymphe, Come to Thy Lover

Thomas Morley
arr. Emma Coulthard

Muzette

Joseph Bodin de Boismortier

Good news for all you recorder players out there! Chester have now brought out **Duets for One** for **Recorder** to join the already popular **Duets for One** series. The book contains 16 tunes in different styles, from *Pachelbel's Canon* to *Killing Me Softly With His Song* and comes with your very own duet partner on CD, plus full demonstration tracks. Arranged by Heather Cox and Garth Rickard.
Order No. CH62865

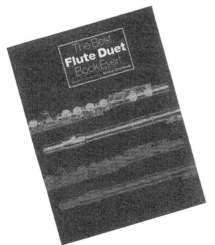

The Best Flute Duet Book Ever! is the first in this highly successful series containing 25 tunes in a variety of different styles! Great for concerts or just for fun, this delightful book is sure to please both the performer and the listener. Selected and arranged by Emma Coulthard.
Order No. CH61694

Devised by Frederick Stocken, **Scale Shapes** is an exciting new diagram-based way to learn piano scales. Unique keyboard diagrams with the fingering on the keys make playing scales easy- left and right hand diagrams appear together. This tried and tested method, saves valuable time in lessons and encourages the pupil to learn by themselves, without constant attention from the teacher.
Also available for Grade 2.
Order No. CH62964

Applause Playalong! - Christmas Songs is just one title in the rapidly expanding series. The book contains ten top Christmas tunes in melody line arrangements plus a CD with demonstration and backing tracks. There are also handy tips and practice points to help you make the most of your performance. All titles in the **Applause** series have been arranged for Flute, Alto Sax, Clarinet and Violin. Other titles include: - **Film Tunes**, **Classic Pop** and **Latino Songs**.
Order No. CH61666